THE BEST OF
BOBBY DA

C000135226

Published by
Wise Publications
8/9 Frith Street, London, W1D 3JB, England.

Exclusive distributors:
Music Sales Limited
Distribution Centre, Newmarket Road, Bury St Edmunds,
Suffolk, IP33 3YB, England.

Music Sales Pty Limited
120 Rothschild Avenue, Rosebery, NSW 2018, Australia.

Order No. AM92017 ISBN 0-7119-4124-6
This book © Copyright 2005 by Wise Publications, a division of Music Sales Limited.

Cover design by Paula Snell.
Cover photographs Michael Ochs Archives/Redferns.
New music arrangements by Jack Long.
Music processed by Paul Ewers Music Design.

Printed in the United Kingdom.

www.musicsales.com

WISE PUBLICATIONS
PART OF THE MUSIC SALES GROUP
London / New York / Paris / Sydney / Copenhagen / Berlin / Madrid / Tokyo

BOBBY DARIN

(1936-1973)

Bobby Darin was one of pop music's great chameleons; a crooner, pop singer, jazz singer and protest singer, at home in cabaret and on the concert stage; a film actor, lover and political commentator; and a business man who understood how, why and where money flows in the music industry. What is all the more remarkable is that he packed all this into a short life, dying at the age of only 37 from heart problems that had dogged him all his days. Told by a doctor that he was unlikely to live beyond the age of 18, it seems he adopted a reckless spirit and determined to live his life to the full before the maker called.

Born Walden Robert Cassotto on 14 May, 1936, in New York, and raised in East Harlem, he attended Hunter College but quit after one semester to become an entertainer. Befriending songwriter and future publishing magnate Don Kirshner, he signed with Decca Records and, after a struggle, made the US charts in 1958 with the novelty hit 'Splash Splash'. In the UK the song was covered by comedian Charlie Drake whose high profile ensured it reached number seven - as opposed to Darin's number 18 – but anyone with ears could tell which was the superior recording.

This little early set back didn't matter. 'Queen Of The Hop', a major US hit, was followed by two number ones, both of which have become standards. Darin's distinctive vocal delivery on 'Dream Lover' was sexually enticing, perfect to attract a legion of girl fans, while his snappy version of the much-covered 'Mack The Knife' remains the most admired rendition of the popular Brecht & Weill song from *The Threepenny Opera*.

The worldwide success of 'Mack The Knife' shifted the balance of Darin's career. The slightly quirky pop singer now became a besuited, finger-popping supper-club entertainer and, somewhat engagingly, he compared himself favourably to the less likeable Frank Sinatra. Other hits followed: his hip take on 'Lazy River', the Hoagy Carmichael standard; the slightly risqué 'Multiplication', about mating; and the catchy 'Things' which was covered by such disparate talents as Marilyn Monroe and Val Doonican. Never one to stay in one place, he recorded pop alongside show tunes and standards, always adding his own touches of cool panache, casual poise and disarming professionalism.

In 1960 he moved into films, starring in *Come September* whose glamorous co-star Sandra Dee he married the same year. He appeared in 13 films in all, and was nominated for an Oscar his role in *Captain Newman MD*. Combining film work and recording, he stepped up a gear to record an album of Ray Charles covers, then turned abruptly left into a sort of quasi-folk protest style, recording Tim Hardin's lovely 'If I Were A Carpenter' (a number 9 UK hit) and John Sebastian's warmly romantic 'Darling Be Home Soon'. Evidently inspired by the earnestness which engulfed pop music in the mid-Sixties, he reverted to his own name with an album titled simply *Born Warden Robert Cossotto*. His next was titled, simply, *Commitment*, which seemed to sum up Darin's entire attitude. A circle had been turned.

Although the hits had dried up by the late Sixties, for the rest of his life Darin continued to be attract big crowds to his shows and command respect from younger artists. Following the assassination of his friend Senator Robert Kennedy in 1968, he considered a career in politics which never materialised. Nevertheless, he took charge of his business affairs with remarkable acuity and might have carved out a career as a successful impresario had fate not intervened.

Bobby Darin married for a second time in 1973, but his happiness was short lived. He died on December 20 the same year following a second bout of open heart surgery, this to replace a valve. In 1990, he was inducted into the Rock and Roll Hall of Fame, which his son Dodd, by Sandra Dee, accepted on his behalf, and in 1999 he was inducted into the Songwriters Hall of Fame.

Recently the subject of the film *Beyond The Sea*, directed, written by and starring Kevin Spacey, Bobby Darin lives on as a figure of unbalanced energy who bestrode the lines between crooners and pop stars and the integrity-driven songwriters who followed. The songs in this folio are the touchstones in one of the most idiosyncratic careers in music.

Chris Charlesworth (April 2005)

AS LONG AS I'M SINGING

WORDS & MUSIC BY BOBBY DARIN

Lyrics:

And if this band don't des - ert____ me, then there's____ no - thing in the

world can hurt____ me____ long as I'm sing - in' my

song.____ Give me trum - pets le - ga - to,

put some sax - es with 'em; strings____ pi - zi - ca - to,____

sing-ing my,___ long as I'm sing-in'_____

___ my_____ song._____

BABY FACE

WORDS & MUSIC BY HARRY AKST & BENNY DAVIS

BEYOND THE SEA

ORIGINAL WORDS & MUSIC BY CHARLES TRENET
ENGLISH WORDS BY JACK LAWRENCE

near be-yond the moon.

I know____ be-yond a doubt,____ my heart____

____ will lead me there____ soon.____ We'll

meet be-yond the shore,____ we'll

13

BILL BAILEY WON'T YOU PLEASE COME HOME

WORDS & MUSIC BY HUGHIE CANNON

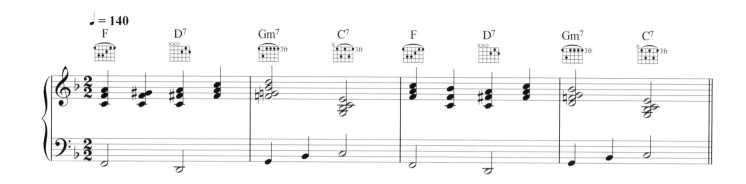

1. On one sum-mer's day the sun was shin-ing fine. The la-dy love of
(2.) wed a B.'n O brake-man that went and threw her down. Hol-ler-ing like a
3. Bill drove by that door in an au-to-mo - bile. A great big dia-mond
(4.) holl-ered through that door "Bill Bail-ey are you sure? Stop a min-ute,

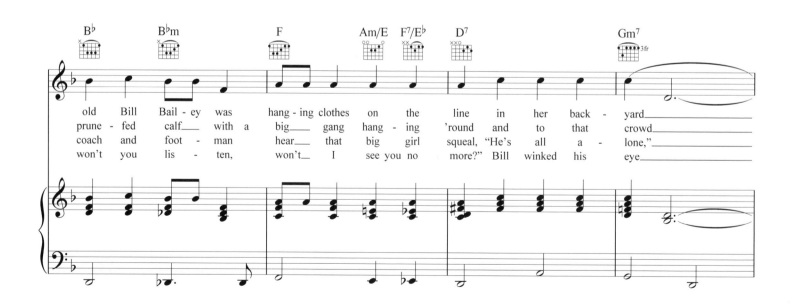

old Bill Bail-ey was hang-ing clothes on the line in her back-yard_____
prune-fed calf with a big__ gang hang-ing 'round and to that crowd_____
coach and foot-man hear__ that big girl squeal, "He's all a-lone,"_____
won't you lis-ten, won't__ I see you no more?" Bill winked his eye_____

17

CLEMENTINE

WORDS & MUSIC BY WOODY HARRIS & PERCY MONTROSE

DREAM LOVER

WORDS & MUSIC BY BOBBY DARIN

Valse moderato

Grazioso

There's a land of charm that I know,
land of sweet ro-mance where I love to go;
And its

In the land of where dreams ne-ver end,
Pa-ra-dise where bro-ken hearts quick-ly mend;
We will

bounds touch my room in the gloom, when the sha - dows creep.
wan - der en - rap - tured and whis - per sweet vows of love.

Some - one I met there waits for me, some - one
Not a cloud to dark - en our sky, not a

ten - der as a lov - er should be; And I whis - per each night as I
care we'll ev - er know, you and I; All the days will be fair with the

Valse lente
CHORUS

close my eyes in sleep.
sun a - shine a - bove.

Dream

lov - er fold your arms a - round me, dream

lov - er your ro - mance has found me, I'm

held in your spell, know - ing too well,

dreams nev - er tell. We

EIGHTEEN YELLOW ROSES

WORDS & MUSIC BY BOBBY DARIN

1. Eight-een yel-low ros-es came to-day,___
(2.) o-pened up the card___ to see what it said,___

HELLO, YOUNG LOVERS

WORDS BY OSCAR HAMMERSTEIN II
MUSIC BY RICHARD RODGERS

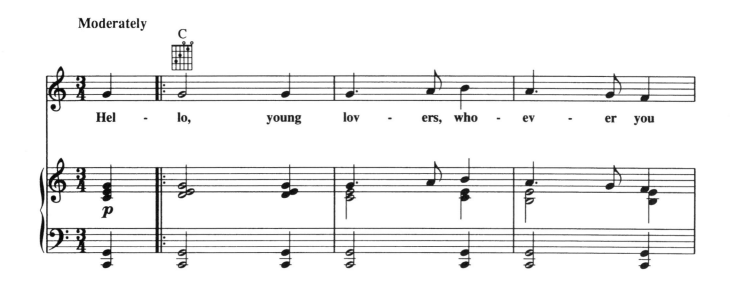

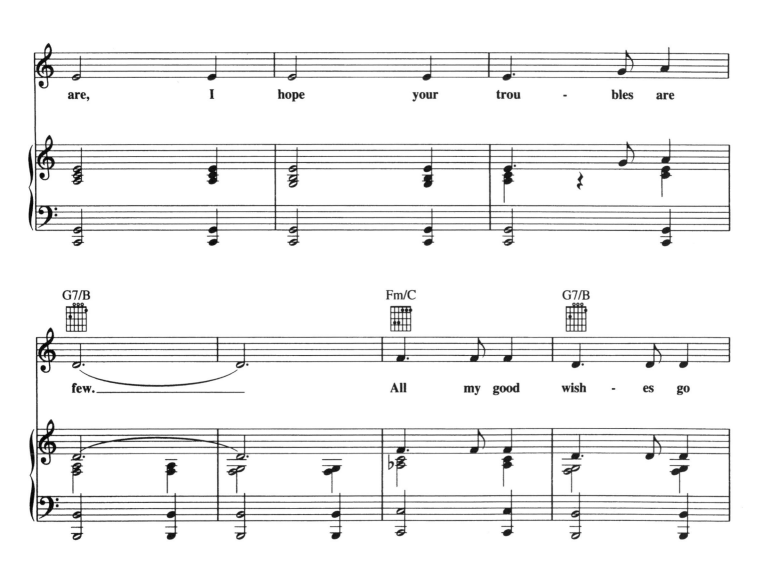

IF I WERE A CARPENTER

WORDS & MUSIC BY TIM HARDIN

MACK THE KNIFE

WORDS BY BERTOLT BRECHT
MUSIC BY KURT WEILL

MULTIPLICATION

WORDS & MUSIC BY BOBBY DARIN

1. When you see a gen-tle-man bee a-round a la-dy bee buzz-ing,
(2.) two but-ter-flies cast-ing their eyes both in the same di-rec-tion.

just____ count to ten then count a-gain: there's
You'd____ nev-er guess that one lit-tle "Yes" could

sure to be an ev-en doz-en!
start a but-ter-fly col-lec-tion!

Mul-ti-pli-ca-

-tion, that's the name of the game;___ and each ge-ne-ra-

-tion, they play it the same.___

2. Now there was

Let me tell you now, I say___ one and one is five;___ you can
Hear me talk-ing to you; Moth-er Na-ture's a clev-er girl,___ she re-

LAZY RIVER

WORDS & MUSIC BY HOAGY CARMICHAEL & SIDNEY ARODIN

QUEEN OF THE HOP

WORDS & MUSIC BY WOODY HARRIS

1. Well, you can talk a-bout your Ju-lie and your Peg-gy Sue;— you can
(2.) wears short shorts and rock 'n' roll shoes.— You

keep your Miss Mol-ly and your Ma-ry Lou;— for when it
ought-a see her dance to The Yel-low Dog Blues.— She's my

comes to The Chick - en or to do - ing The Bop,___
su - gar - time ba - by, I'm her lol - li - pop.___

I got___ a girl they call The Queen of the Hop.___
Ev - 'ry - bo - dy knows I love my Queen of the Hop.___
Oh well, I

love my___ Queen...
Do you know who I mean?___

Sweet lit - tle six - teen:___
yes,___

does The Stroll. *(Instrumental)*

D.S. al Coda

Oh well, she

Coda

does The Stroll.. Oh well, I love my Queen.

RAININ'

WORDS & MUSIC BY BOBBY DARIN

SPLISH SPLASH

WORDS & MUSIC BY BOBBY DARIN & JEAN MURRAY

how was I to know there was a par - ty go - ing on?
went and put my danc - ing shoes

on I was a - splish - in' and a - splash - in', I was a -

roll - in' and a - stroll - in', I was a - mov - in' and a - groov - in',

Repeat and Fade

I was a - reel - in' with the feel - in' I was a -

69

THINGS

WORDS & MUSIC BY BOBBY DARIN

Ev-'ry night_ I sit here by_ my win-dow,_ (win-dow)_ star-ing at_ the lone-ly a-ve-nue,_ (a-ve-nue)_

things   like a sail-boat ride. (Yeah, yeah). What a-bout___ the night we cried?

Things   like a lov-er's_ vow;_____ things   that we don't do now;_____

think-ing__ 'bout__ the things___ we used to do.__

Still can hear_ the juke-box_ soft-ly play-ing,__   (play-ing),__ and the

things like a sail-boat ride. (Whoah, woah). What a-bout___ the night we cried?

Things like a lov-er's___ vow;_____ things that we

don't do now;___ think-ing___ 'bout___ the things___ we used to do.___

And___ heart-aches are the things___ I'm talk-ing___ to.___

YOU MUST HAVE BEEN
A BEAUTIFUL BABY

WORDS & MUSIC BY HARRY WARREN & JOHNNY MERCER